I0801345

WHAT GROWS ON TREES?

Written by Karen Hoenecke
Illustrated by Gary Bialke

Do apples grow on trees?
Yes.

Do cats grow on trees?
No.

Do oranges grow on trees?
Yes.

Do hamburgers grow on trees?
No.

Do cherries grow on trees?
Yes.

Do rabbits grow on trees?
No.

Does money grow on trees?
NO!

Stop being so silly,
will you please?

Do more with WHAT GROWS ON TREES?

- Talk to your child about the many kinds of fruit and nuts that grow on trees. How many can he or she name? Encourage your child to draw a fruit tree laden with fruit, and help him or her label the picture with the name of the fruit.

- Show your child how to tally objects by fives by making four vertical lines and a diagonal line. Then as you take a walk together around the neighborhood, have your child keep track of the trees in groups of five. When you return home, help him or her to count the total number of trees you saw on your walk.

- Have your child collect leaves from various trees. Ask your child to sort the leaves by shape, color, or size and to explain how the leaves are alike or different.